FRANCINE

DAN

HENRY

LADYBIRD BOOKS, INC.
Auburn, Maine 04210 U.S.A.
© LADYBIRD BOOKS LTD 1991
Loughborough, Leicestershire, England

Printed in England (3)

Little Bunnies
On Vacation

By Norma Daniels
Illustrated by Carolyn Bracken

Ladybird Books

Getting Ready

The little Bunnies and their friends
are all packing for their vacations.

binoculars

knapsack

fishing tackle

hiking boots

straw hat

picnic basket

golf clubs

sandals

tennis racket

toothbrush

camera

suitcase

film

sunglasses

diving mask

bathing suit

suntan lotion

pail and shovel

flippers

Getting There

They'll all be on their way soon!

BY CAR

roof rack

road map

tool kit

spare tire

station wagon

BY PLANE

flight attendant

check-in counter

conveyor belt

departure lounge

luggage

security area

BY TRAIN

notice board

conductor

porter

platform

baggage wagon

ARRIVALS		DEPARTURES	
OAKDALE	10pm	SHORE PTS.	11m.
CARROTVILLE	11m		
LETTUCEBERG	11m		

BY BUS

TO THE COUNTRY

ticket window

GO BY BUS

hold

bus driver

vending machine

In the Mountains

The Bunnies drive up a winding mountain road.
"I see a deer," says Mom.
"And I see a skunk!" cries Billy.

lake

skunk

mountain

e lookout tower

forest

trail

hiker

road

sign

deer

fawn

waterfall

stream

raccoon

Camping Out

At the campsite, Billy helps Mom set up the tent, while Betsy tries out her new fishing rod.
"I think I've caught something!" Betsy shouts.

fishing rod

beans

fork

hot dogs

frying p

stove

marshmallows

campfire

lantern

tent

flashlight

sleeping bags

air mattress

In the Country

Dan Kitten enjoys watching the countryside from the bus window. "Hi, little bird!" he calls.

farm

brook

songbird

wildflowers

windmill

orchard

meadow

bridge

butterfly

On the Farm

Everyone helps out at the Kitten Cousins' farm.
Well, almost everyone—Dan's father is off to play golf!

weather vane

field

silo

haylot

barn

sheep

horse

lamb

hay

pitchfork

pig

piglets

cow

calf

At the Seashore

What a beautiful sand castle Francine Fox has built!
"Would you like this starfish to decorate it?"
asks her new friend, Lester Pig.

lighthouse

lifeguard

sea gull

rubber raft

sand castle

shovel

starfish

crab

pail

seaweed

beach house

beach umbrella

sand dune

rubber tube

beach chair

driftwood

At the Amusement Park

balloon

roller coaster

"Aim the ball carefully," says Francine's father,
"and maybe you can win a teddy bear!"

merry-go-round

BALL TOSS • RING TOSS

prizes

bumper cars

cotton candy

3 BALLS or RINGS FOR $1.

Ferris wheel

FUN HOUSE

FORTUNES

MADAME ZAZA

fortune teller

ice cream

POPCORN

50¢

In the City

The doorman takes a picture of the
Bear family outside their hotel.

skyscrapers

BLOOMINGBEA

museum

department store

subway
entrance

sidewalk café

park

BUS
STOP

TAXI

taxi

traffic jam

apartment building

BLOOMINGBEARS

hotel

DON'T WALK

PHONE

police officer

BEARVERLY HOTEL

traffic light

telephone booth

parking meter

"Everyone say cheese, please!" he says.

At the Theater

The Bears have good seats for a matinee performance of *The Pussycat Princess*. Henry is thrilled to see his favorite actress, Patti Purr, in person.

curtain

scenery

boxes

backstage

orchestra

EXIT

stage

footlights

actor

actress

costume

spotlight

chandelier

usher

audience

balcony

EXIT

EXIT

critic

aisle

program

At the Museum

PAINTING AND SCULPTURE

painting

DINOSAURS

suit of armor

dinosaur bones

MONA LIZARD

DOGAS

statue

Henry rushes over to the suit of armor. "There was a knight like that in the play yesterday!" he exclaims.

MUMMIES

mummy

guard

GIFT SHOP

vase

POSTCARDS

display case

Home Again

Vacation time is over for the Bunnies and their friends. Now it's time to share happy memories—and think about where to go next year!

sea shell

photograph album

souven

pine cone

pressed flowers

HONEY

METROPOLIS
MUSEUM — T-shirt

picture postcards

photographs

BILLY   BETSY

DAD   SAM   MOM